CW00665187

Printed and bound in Great Britain by Caligraving Limited Thetford Norfolk

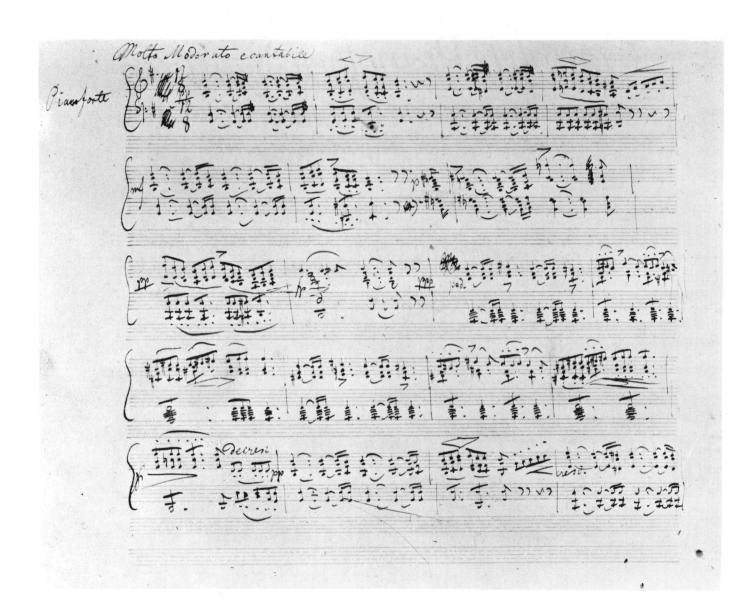

Facsimile of Schubert's autograph of the opening of Sonata in G, D.894 (reproduced by kind permission of The British Library Board). Note the altered rhythm in bars 1 and 3, and the many missing ties in r.h. chords.

SCHUBERT

Complete Pianoforte Sonatas

including the unfinished works

Edited, annotated and fingered by

HOWARD FERGUSON

Volume III

THE ASSOCIATED BOARD OF
THE ROYAL SCHOOLS OF MUSIC

CONTENTS
Volume I

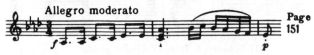

Volume II

CHRONOLOGICAL TABLE OF SCHUBERT'S PIANO SONATAS

Sonatas	Unfinished Sonatas	Date	Sources
EARLY PERIOD			
	App. 1 E major, D. 157	Feb. 1815	Autograph
	App. 2 C major, D. 279	Sept. 1815	Autograph
1. E major, D. 459		Aug. 1816	Autograph of I & part of II; 1st ed., [1843]
2. A minor, D. 537		Mar. 1817	Autograph
	App. 3 A flat major, D. 557	May 1817	Autograph of I, II & part of III; MS copy
	App. 4 E minor, D. 566	June 1817	Autograph of I & III (Trio only); 1st ed. of II, 1907, and III (Scherzo only), 1928
	App 5 E minor, D².769A (= D¹.994)	c. 1823	Autograph
3a. D flat major, D. 567		June 1817	Autograph, lacks last 17 bars of finale
3b. E flat major, D. 568		June-Nov. 1817	1st ed., 1829
	App. 6 F sharp minor, D. 571	July 1817	Autograph
4. B major, D. 575		Aug. 1817	Autograph sketch; MS copy; 1st ed., [c. 1844]
	App. 7 C major, D. 613	Apr. 1818	Autograph
	App. 8 F minor, D. 625 & 505	Sept. 1818	MS copy
	App. 9 C sharp minor, D. 655	Apr. 1819	Autograph
5. A major, D. 664		? July 1819	1st ed., 1829
MIDDLE PERIOD			
6. A minor, D. 784		Feb. 1823	Autograph
	App. 10 C major, D. 840	Apr. 1825	Part autograph; 1st ed., [1861]
7. A minor, D. 845		early 1825	1st ed., [1826]
8. D major, D. 850		Aug. 1825	Autograph; 1st ed., [1826]
9. G major, D. 894		Oct. 1826	Autograph; 1st ed., [1827]

Published during Schubert's lifetime (bracket spanning nos. 7, 8, 9)

Sonatas	Unfinished Sonatas	Date	Sources
LATE PERIOD			
10. C minor, D. 958		Sept. 1828	Autograph
11. A major, D. 959		Sept. 1828	Autograph
12. B flat major, D. 960		Sept. 1828	Autograph

The D-numbers refer to the chronological order proposed in O. E. Deutsch's

Franz Schubert: Thematische Verzeichnis seiner Werke in chronologischer Folge, 2nd edition; Bärenreiter, Kassel 1979.

INTRODUCTION

FRANZ SCHUBERT

(1797-1828)

Although Schubert's working life lasted for little more than a dozen years, the twelve Piano Sonatas that he completed can nevertheless be grouped into the usual three periods, namely: early, middle, and late. Together they form a series that is unsurpassed in scope save by the 32 Sonatas of Beethoven; and if the earliest, the Sonata in E, D. 459, lacks the effortless mastery of the finest songs from the same period—such as the setting of Goethe's 'Erlkönig', D.328—the second, the A minor, D. 537, shows that Schubert by the age of 20 had already found his own way of dealing with the larger instrumental forms.

In addition to the twelve completed works there are ten unfinished Sonatas ranging in length from a few dozen bars to a four-movement work that lacks little besides its 1st-movement recapitulation. These fragments are of great interest, not only for the sake of the complete movements they contain, but also for the light they throw on Schubert's oddly hit-or-miss method of working. They have therefore been included in the present edition as Appendices to Volumes 1 & 2, where chronologically they belong. (There are no fragments from the late period.) Also included are several movements that may or may not belong to the unfinished Sonatas with which they have been associated at one time or another. Thus the edition contains twenty-one complete movements over and above those belonging to the familiar twelve Sonatas.

The unfinished movements have been left as they stand; for experience has shown that even the most skilful editorial completion is likely to betray its lack of authenticity at some point—generally where harmonic adjustment is required by an added recapitulation. This, however, should not deter the player from trying his hand at finishing them for himself; for on doing so he will gain invaluable insights into the completed movements that he must use as his models.

The differing numbering of the Sonatas in various editions is due to several related facts. Firstly, only three of the works were published during Schubert's lifetime; secondly, the opus numbers given by publishers to posthumously printed works bore no relation to chronology; thirdly, some Sonatas were still unknown when the relevant volume of the Breitkopf & Härtel *Gesammtausgabe* first appeared in 1888; and lastly, the later 'popular' editions differed in the works they included. There was, indeed, no generally accepted chronology until the publication in 1951 of O. E. Deutsch's *Schubert: thematic catalogue of all his works*. The order in the present edition is based on Deutsch's dating; but the completed Sonatas are numbered in one series, as 1 to 12, and those that are unfinished in another, as Appendix 1 to Appendix 10. (See the Chronological Table opposite.)

SOURCES

The Chronological Table also lists in summary form each Sonatas's source(s), of which fuller details are given in the Notes preceding individual works. For the twelve complete Sonatas they are as follows:–

> Autograph: Sonatas No. 2, 3a, 6, 8, 9, 10, 11 & 12 (8 in all).
> Part-autograph & 1st edition: Sonatas No. 1 & 4 (2 in all).
> 1st edition alone: Sonatas No. 3b, 5 & 7 (3 in all).

Only Sonatas No. 7, 8 & 9 were published during Schubert's lifetime, and of these Nos. 8 & 9 also exist in autograph. It is particularly unfortunate that there is no autograph of No. 7, for the 1st edition (the only source) contains such blatant errors that it is impossible to believe that Schubert saw the proofs. Four Sonatas, Nos. 1, 3b, 4 & 5, rely either wholly or in part on posthumous editions that appear to be much less inaccurate. Other later editions have no textual significance, as they are all based on one or other of the above.

Most of the unfinished Sonatas have survived in autograph; but App. 3, 4, 8 & 10 are derived wholly or in part from either MS copies or posthumous editions. The copyist of App. 3 & 8 (both are from the same hand) was notably inaccurate; but the 1st editions of App. 4 (2nd movement) and App. 10 appear to be reliable.

TEXTUAL PROBLEMS

Schubert's autographs look remarkably clear at first sight, considering the speed at which he worked (see the Frontispiece to Volume I). Yet closer examination shows that they are often ambiguous with regard to slurs and ties, dynamics, and accidentals.

Slurs and ties. Slurs are at times so carelessly drawn that it is impossible to tell where they are meant to begin and end. An editor must be more precise; but it should be remembered that his decisions may not always be correct.

The phrasing of identical passages in an exposition and recapitulation is often different. No attempt has been made to iron out such differences, even when they appear to be due to no more than haste or momentary carelessness.

Like most classical composers, Schubert often uses slurs to divide a long legato phrase into shorter units, each generally ending at a barline. Though they do not necessarily imply a break in the legato, these slurs have been reproduced as they appear in the sources.

In order to save himself time and trouble, Schubert habitually left out some of the necessary signs when tying one chord to another. Provided the chords are identical his meaning is likely to be clear, as can be seen from the opening of the Sonata in G, D. 894 (Vol. III, No. 9), where editorial ties are marked with a cross-stroke. His intentions are less certain, however, when he uses a *slur* (not a tie) to join two slightly different chords, as in the 2nd movement of the Sonata in D, D. 859 (Vol. III, No. 8). Strictly speaking, all the notes in the second chord of the latter pairs should be sounded. Yet at times, though not always, it seems that Schubert again expected one sign to fulfil a dual function: namely, to slur the two chords together and also to tie the notes they shared. Such cases must be judged in their context in order to determine what was intended. The editor's conclusions are shown by the presence or absence of cross-stroke ties; but the player should feel free to disagree.

Dynamics. Schubert was far less careful about dynamic markings than, say, Beethoven. For example, an accent (>) is often indistinguishable from a hairpin *dim.* ($\Longrightarrow$); consequently the engravers of early editions frequently mistook one sign for the other. As this can still happen, the player should remember that any printed accent in the present edition *may* be a misreading of a hairpin *dim.*, and *vice versa*.

Another puzzling mark is the compound sign *fp* $\Longrightarrow$. Paul Badura-Skoda has suggested, in his excellent edition of the *Impromptus, Moments Musicaux & Drei Klavierstücke* (Universal, Vienna 1969), that it means *f* $\Longrightarrow$ *p*. Though no proof exists, this may well be true.

Inconsistencies occur from time to time. Thus a *pp* may be followed by a long *dim.*, only to end up with another *pp*; or a *f cresc.* may lead to no more than another *f*. (This is quite different from Beethoven's *p cresc.* followed by a *p* (*subito* implied).) In such cases the player must use his own judgement to decide at what level the passage begins and ends, and how the *dim.* or *cresc.* should be spaced out.

Accidentals. Schubert's notation of accidentals is always idiosyncratic and often careless. When a passage extends over several octaves within a single bar, he generally writes the necessary accidentals only in the first octave, leaving the remainder to be supplied by the player or the engraver (in the present edition they have been added in small type). Moreover, he sometimes expects accidentals to remain in force across the barline; and not infrequently he forgets them altogether. Generally his intentions are clear. For example, in the Sonata in C minor, D. 958 (Vol. III, No. 10), 4th movement, bb. 636–643, there can be no doubt that all the Ds must be flattened editorially, since the key is now A flat; and in the Sonata in B flat, D. 960 (Vol. III, No. 12), 1st movement, bb. 45–46, it is equally obvious that all the As should be flattened. Very occasionally, however, it is hard to be certain what was intended. The most puzzling instance is in the same Sonata in B flat, 2nd movement, bb. 10 & 99, where it is very difficult to decide whether Schubert really intended the arguably uncharacteristic 1st r.h. chord that appears in both the sketch and the fair copy, or whether he forgot to add a double-sharp to the F in each bar simply because it *was* so obvious. The pros and cons of such cases are set forth in the preliminary Notes to the Sonata concerned, so that the player can make up his own mind.

The Instrument

The piano for which Schubert wrote had a compass of six octaves from the F an octave below the bass stave to F two octaves above the treble. In the unfinished Sonata in F minor, D. 625 (Vol. II, App. 8), two passages in the Scherzo go three semitones higher, to G sharp; but the only source of the work is a rather unreliable copyist's MS, which may not reproduce the original accurately. The upward limit caused Schubert no problems, but he must often have regretted the restricted range of the bass. This can be felt in passages such as bb. 216 & 218 in the 1st movement of the Sonata in D flat, D. 567 (Vol. I, No. 3a), where the l.h. theme has had to be distorted because of the lack of a low D flat. It can also be seen in the 'Reliquie' Sonata, D. 840 (Vol. II, App. 10), 1st movement, bb. 28, 32, 34, etc., where the lack of several bass octaves completely upsets the tonal balance. In the present edition such 'missing' notes have been added either in small type or within square brackets. But the player should feel free to ignore them if he finds they introduce a disturbingly alien tone-colour on the instrument he happens to be using.

Apart from compass, the main difference between modern instruments and both the grand and the 'square' pianos of Schubert's day is that the latter were far lighter in both touch and tone. Players will be most aware of this in the passages of quick repeated notes or chords, of which Schubert was so fond. These would not have been specially difficult on the old instruments with their light and shallow touch; but for the modern pianist they become a considerable technical feat. When tackling them it is important (a) to avoid stiffening the forearm; (b) to think of the repetitions not from note to note, but in groups that reflect some aspect of the rhythmic pattern; and (c) to relax quite consciously at predetermined points, such as rhythmically 'weak' notes following main beats, changes in the pattern of movement and so on.

Close-position bass chords must be played with great care on the modern piano if a muddy and opaque sound is to be avoided. The most obvious solution is to lighten the middle notes of the chord, so that they are less prominent than the outer notes. But at times it may be found better—particularly if a strong yet transparent accent is required—to break the chord slightly: i.e. to play it as a very quick arpeggio.

Pedalling

Schubert used the signs *Ped.*, *Pedale*, or *con Pedale* for the sustaining pedal, and *con sordini* for the *una corda*. They appear infrequently; and since no editorial pedal marks have been added to the text, the player must decide for himself (with occasional help from the preliminary Notes) where, and how much, additional pedalling is required.

Tempo

The sonata movements of Schubert, unlike those of Haydn, Mozart and Beethoven, often require more than a single basic tempo: for a speed that fits (say) the opening of a movement may make the 2nd subject-group sound too fast, and one that suits the latter may make the opening too slow. The changes needed are generally very slight; and since they should always be imperceptible, the player must aim to give the *impression* of a consistent tempo throughout a movement, by making (wherever possible) a gradual transition from one tempo to the other. Suggested metronome marks are given in the preliminary Notes to each Sonata: but they are neither authoritative nor binding. Their purpose is *not* to prescribe the speed at which a particular section must be played, but rather to indicate where changes are likely to occur, and how small they need be.

Schubert's procedures are always leisurely, so the player should resist every temptation to speed-up a movement merely because he imagines it is over-long.

Staccato Dots (ˌ) and Wedges (ˈ)

These two signs are clearly differentiated in the autographs, where the wedge is always written as a thin downward stroke. It seems likely that Schubert uses the wedge in its pre-Beethoven sense of an accent, either with or without a staccato; and that it often indicates an intermediate stage between the two, as in the Sonata in D, D. 850 (Vol. III, No. 8), 2nd movement, bb. 165-168, where the *ff* chords are marked thus :-

[musical example]

Rhythmic Conventions

Another early practice followed by Schubert is the convention of adjusting dotted duple rhythms to coincide with triplets when the two occur simultaneously. In the autograph of the song 'Erstarrung' (*Winterreise*, D. 911, No. 4, b. 24, etc.) he writes [musical figure]; and in the Sonatas the two rhythms are frequently aligned visually. For example, in the Sonata in B flat, D. 960 (Vol. III, No. 12), 2nd movement, b.52, etc., both the autograph and 1st edition show the two r.h. parts thus :- [musical figure] as undoubtedly they were meant to be played; yet almost all subsequent editions alter this to :- [musical figure]. At times, however, it seems likely that the two conflicting rhythms should be given their true value — particularly when a dotted duple theme has already been established in a duple context, as in the same Sonata in B flat, 4th movement, b. 185, etc. In the present edition, passages requiring adjustment are aligned as they appear in the source concerned, with the probable rhythmic interpretation indicated in small notes above or below the stave. Since the correct interpretation is occasionally in doubt, the player should feel free to follow his own instinct if he finds that it conflicts with the suggestions of the editor.

Ornamentation

Six different ornaments occur in the Sonatas: shakes, inverted mordents, turns, arpeggios, single small notes, and groups of small notes.

Shake: tr. Shakes start on the main note, unless the contrary is indicated. This interpretation is given in J.N. Hummel's Pianoforte School (*Ausführliche theoretische practische Anweisung zum Pianoforte-Spiel*, 1828), which, like all such treatises, reflects an already established practice. Moreover, it is not unreasonable to suppose that Schubert was in agreement with it, since he was an admirer of Hummel and planned to dedicate the last three Sonatas to him.

Inverted Mordent: ⌇ . From the Sonata in A minor, D. 845 (Vol. II, No. 7), 1st movement, bb. 248-252 & 257-261, it can be seen that [figure] equals [figure], for either sign is used in identical passages. Generally, though perhaps not invariably, it should begin on the beat, thus: [figure] .

Turn: ∞ . Whether written above a note or between two notes, a turn starts with the upper auxiliary, thus :-

or some rhythmic variation of the same note-pattern.

Arpeggio: ∤ . In theory, arpeggios always begin on the beat. But where the top note requires special emphasis, as in the Sonata in A minor, D. 784 (Vol. II, No. 6), 2nd movement, bb. 32-33, etc., it may be found preferable to make the top note coincide with the beat.

Single small note: ♪, ♪, ♪. Paul Badura-Skoda has pointed out in his edition of the *Impromptus* (see above) that in Schubert's songs a single small note is often used in the voice part to indicate a long appoggiatura, whereas the same appoggiatura is shown in the piano accompaniment at its true value, i.e. as a normal-sized note. Hence it appears that a single small note in a piano work is usually intended to be a short, unaccented acciaccatura (♪); moreover, the following passage from the Sonata in G, D. 894 (Vol. III, No. 9), 1st movement, b. 76, shows that it is likely to anticipate the beat :-

. Occasionally, however, the context suggests that a single small note is intended (even in a piano work) as an expressively accentuated long appoggiatura *on* the beat: for example, in the same Sonata in G, 2nd movement, b. 49, and 3rd movement, b. 58. Though this interpretation is less common, its possible occurrence should be borne in mind.

Group of small notes: ♫, ♬, ♬, etc. As noted above, the written-out inverted mordent (♬) begins on the beat. But with other groups of small notes the context generally suggests that they should anticipate the beat. This can be seen from the passages such as the following :-

Sonata in E flat, D. 568   Sonata in C minor, D. 958
2nd movement, b. 31   2nd movement, b. 26

In the first, the accent on the r.h. top B flat would be ineffective were it not to coincide with the l.h. chord; and in the second, the octave layout of the r.h. melody would be interrupted, and its accent lost, if the pair of gracenotes were to begin on the beat.

This Edition

As already stated, the Notes preceding each Sonata give details of the source(s) used; otherwise they are devoted mainly to questions of performance and study. In the music pages, numbered footnotes deal with textual matters, and lettered footnotes with the interpretation of ornaments, etc., at their first appearance in each movement. Redundant accidentals have been omitted. Editorial accidentals, notes, rests, dynamics, etc., are printed either in small type or within square brackets, and editorial slurs, ties, and 'hairpin' *cresc.* & *dim.* signs are crossed with a small vertical stroke. Curved brackets indicate notes that should not be struck. Fingering has been added throughout, as there is none in the original sources other than in bb. 56 & 181 of the 3rd movement of Sonata in A, D. 664.

Schubert's distribution of notes on the two staves has not always been followed. Like many other keyboard composers, he tended to avoid the use of leger-lines and clef-changes by writing all notes *above* middle-C on the upper stave, and all notes *below* middle-C on the lower. The result is often confusing for the player: for at times the whole texture is crammed on to a single stave, and chords and melodies lose their visual shape through being divided between the two staves. Since this aspect of the original does not appear to have any musical significance, the editor has felt free to alter the layout whenever doing so would make it easier to read. Generally his aim has been to place r.h. notes on the upper stave and l.h. notes on the lower; but occasionally it has been more convenient to use the signs ⌊ and ⌈ to indicate the r.h. and l.h. respectively.

Acknowledgements

The task of tracking down the sources was greatly simplified by the information contained in Otto Erich Deutsch's *Schubert: thematic catalogue of all his works* (Dent, London 1951), and Maurice J.E. Brown's article 'Towards an edition of Schubert's piano sonatas' in his *Essays on Schubert* (Macmillan, London 1966). I would like to record more personal debts of gratitude to the late Maurice Brown, who before his lamented death replied to a number of queries regarding the present whereabouts of autographs; and to Dr Walter Dürr, editor-in-chief of the *Neue Schubert Ausgabe,* who not only answered various questions concerning sources, but most thoughtfully lent me (unasked) a photocopy of the autograph of the unfinished Sonata in A flat, D. 557, whose present whereabouts are unknown.

Thanks are due to the following for providing microfilms or photocopies of autographs, MSS, and/or 1st editions in their possession, and for permission to publish :- The British Library Board; The Syndics of The Fitzwilliam Museum, Cambridge; the Bibliothèque Nationale, Paris; the Deutsche Staatsbibliothek, Musikabteilung, Berlin; the Staatsbibliothek Preussischer Kulturbesitz, Berlin; the Stadtbibliothek, Leipzig; the Oesterreichische Nationalbibliothek, Vienna; the Stadtbibliothek, Vienna; the Gesellschaft der Musikfreunde, Vienna; and the Library of Congress, Washington. The Universitetsbibliotek, Lund, courteously provided facilities for me to consult the autograph of the Sonata in A minor, D. 784, and the MS copy of the Sonata in B, D. 575, of which (by the strange terms of a bequest) they were not permitted to supply photographs. Finally, Dr Georg Floersheim, of Basel, was persuaded to authorize The Library of Congress, Washington, to provide me with a microfilm of the autograph of the last three Sonatas, D. 958-960, of which he is the present owner.

The Oxford University Press has kindly given permission for the use of some material from my Introduction to *Schubert: a selection (Oxford Keyboard Classics),* ed. Stephen Bishop (O.U.P., London 1972), and from my book, *Keyboard Interpretation* (O.U.P., London 1975).

HOWARD FERGUSON
Cambridge 1972-76

Addendum

Since these three volumes were prepared for the press, two important publications have appeared: 1) Otto Erich Deutsch, *Franz Schubert: Thematische Verzeichnis seiner Werke in chronologischer Folge,* 2nd Edition; Bärenreiter, Kassel 1979. (Referred to as D².). 2) Ernst Hilmar, *Verzeichnis der Schubert-Handschriften in der Musiksammlung der Wiener Stadt- und Landesbibliotehk;* Bärenreiter, Kassel 1978. According to the former, the following emendations should be made in Vol. I of the present edition: Sonata in E, D.459, consists in fact of two works: movements I & II=Unfinished Sonata in E, D.459; and movements III-V=*Drei Klavierstücke,* D².459A. Sonata in D flat, D.567, can be dated June 1817. Unfinished Sonata in E minor, D.994, has been re-numbered D².769A, with the suggested date of *c.* 1823 in place of ?1817.

H.F.   1978

8. SONATA in D, D.850

A Autograph, headed 'Sonate' and dated August 1825. (Vienna, Oesterreichische Nationalbibliothek.)

B 1st edition: *Seconde Grande Sonate*, Op. 53; M. Artaria, Vienna [1826]. Dedicated by Schubert to the pianist C.M. de Bocklet.

Apparently B was printed from yet another source, C, which no longer exists: for A contains no engraver's marks, and B differs from it in a number of details. A few of these are significant and undoubtedly originated with the composer. Nevertheless, A provides the more reliable basic text, since the number of misprints in B suggest that Schubert saw no proofs.

The present edition follows A, except where B provides a variant reading that is likely to have originated with Schubert. Significant differences between A and B—but *not* details of phrasing and articulation—are listed in the footnotes.

I Allegro [♩ = c. 76 & 66]

Bar 1 (♩ = c. 76).—Schubert was undecided about the tempo indication, for the surviving autograph is marked 'Allegro, ₵' (i.e. two-in-a-bar), whereas the 1st edition has 'Allegro vivace, C' (four-in-a-bar). The original half-bar beat seems preferable, since the groups of four repeated quavers (8th-notes) in the opening subject and elsewhere must be treated as single units: that is to say, each group should have a slight *cresc.* leading to the following beat, rather than an accent on the 1st & 3rd quavers.

12–15.—The repeated quavers in the l.h. lead to the middle of the bar, and those in the r.h. to the 1st beat. Thus the stresses alternate between the l.h. & r.h. minims (half-notes).

32.—Do not miss the unexpected *p* in the middle of the bar.

34.—In accordance with the old convention, the l.h. dotted rhythm on the 2nd crotchet (quarter-note) should be adjusted to coincide with the prevailing triplet rhythm of the r.h., as shown below the stave.

35, 41, 43, 47, & 48–54.—Similar adjustments are probably intended here, to match the surrounding triplets.

48 (♩ = c. 66).—The unusual indication 'e con cappriccio' (*sic*) implies some rhythmic freedom. Though omitted from all previous editions, and almost obliterated in the autograph by alterations to the phrasing, there is no doubt that Schubert did *not* strike out the three words.

54.—A slight *accel.* leading back to

55 (♩ = c. 76).—*tempo primo*.

95–163.—The development falls into two main sections :– (1) the action-packed bb. 95–143, and (2) the tranquil and rhythmically uneventful bb. 144–151, which, in spite of their apparent calm, are moving gradually towards the mounting excitement of a long dominant preparation, bb. 152–162, that ends with the climatic recapitulation at b. 163. Within section (1) are the following contrasts of phrase-structure, texture, and 'orchestration' :–

95–103 (beginning at the half-bar).—4 bars of *marcato* trumpets and horns—do not obscure the rests with pedal— answered by 4 bars of full orchestra.

103–111.—The same 8-bar pattern, with added fragments of triplet counter-point at first in the r.h. and then in the l.h.

111–117.—On a slightly lower dynamic level, 2+4 bars with continuous triplet counterpoint; plus a 1-bar *dim.* leading to

118–124.—the same pattern of 6 bars plus 1 bar, but with the dynamics reversed: i.e. *pp* (for the first time in the movement), ending with a 1-bar [*molto*] *cresc.*

125–128.—2+2 bars, full orchestra, with the main interest at first in the r.h. and then in the l.h.

129–132.—3 bars of nothing but triplets; plus a cadential bar leading to

133–140.—the same 8-bar pattern as bb. 125–132, but a tone higher.

141–144.—The cadential bar is repeated in rising steps of a semitone, and finally closes, with an interrupted cadence, into section (2).

246 (♩ = c. 88).—i.e. only slightly faster than *tempo primo*.

II Andante con moto [♩ = c. 58]

The words 'con moto' show that the opening theme must not drag. Nevertheless it should be sufficiently spacious to allow the accompanying figuration at the return (b. 85*f*) to sound unhurried. To find a convincing tempo, start by playing the return rather than the opening. Think of three slow beats in a bar (not six), make the upper l.h. part warmly melodic, and keep the r.h. figuration light. When the latter begins to fall into place, try the beginning of the movement at exactly the same speed. If it flows easily, the tempo is correct. If not, go back to the return and take it a fraction quicker, but not quickly enough to make the r.h. sound rushed. Then once again try the opening, but at the revised speed. If it still fails to flow, continue to experiment with slightly different tempi, until finally you light on the one that sounds and feels exactly right for both appearances of the theme.

Two further problems of interpretation are concerned with (1) ties and slurs, and (2) two-note ornaments.

(1) See the Introduction, p. 7, regarding Schubert's unconventional use of ties and slurs. In the present movement the choice of editorial ties has been determined by the following considerations. Firstly, in the 2nd half of b. 4 the tied As in the l.h. show that the equivalent As in the opening half-bar should also be tied. Secondly, if chord 3 of the first full bar is played exactly as shown in the autograph, the tied C-sharp will be too weak to balance the remaining notes. To preserve euphony either the C-sharp must be repeated, or the lower parts in both hands tied. But since Schubert has specifically ruled out the first of these alternatives, it follows that he must have intended the second. It would seem, too, that the convention applies to the whole of the opening theme, i.e. as far as b. 42. Not to the return (b. 85*f*), however, where the lack of l.h. ties is probably an anticipation of the still more distinct r.h. articulation at b. 93*f*. (The editorial ties in l.h. b. 87 & r.h. b. 95 have been added by analogy with l.h. b. 89).

If the player does not agree with this reasoning he can ignore the editorial ties and repeat the notes concerned.

(2) In the Sonata in A minor, D. 845 (see Vol. 2, No. 7), Schubert undoubtedly intended ♫♩ and ♩ to mean exactly the same thing, viz. ♫ (beginning on the beat). Here, however, he appears to distinguish between the two. In b. 3 the 3-note ornament (a written-out inverted turn) almost certainly precedes the beat, otherwise the octave doubling of the melody would be momentarily obscured. Hence it is probable that the 2-note ornament found in similar contexts (bb. 33, 88 & 125) should do likewise. In bb. 111–113, on the other hand, the inverted mordent ᨈ occurs in both parts, and can therefore be played *on* the beat, as usual, without disturbing the octave doubling.

III Scherzo & Trio: Allegro vivace [♩ = c. 160]

The first five notes of the ubiquitous figure [♪] ♫. ♫. ♪ | ♩ together form an 'upbeat' that leads, with a slight overall *cresc.*, to the following minim (half-note). Keep the semiquavers (16th-notes) light; and where chords are involved (e.g. in the opening bar, and in bb. 20, 24, 44–46, 50, etc.) play them as though each short-long pair required only one up-and-down movement of the hand, quite close to the keys, rather than two downward movements.

16 & 18.—Notice that here and in the recapitulation r.h. note 2 is a quaver (8th-note), not a semiquaver.

44–45.—A slight accent on b. 44 beat 2, and b. 45 beats 1 & 3, to show the cross-rhythm.

50*f*.—To match the relaxed mood of this typically Schubertian waltz, the tempo can be very slightly eased—to, say, ♩ = c. 152. In spite of the *Ped.* indication, no more than a touch of pedal on every 2nd beat is needed. This will help to underline the characteristic Viennese lilt, which can be further enhanced by fractionally delaying the 2nd crotchet (quarter-note) of every alternate bar (i.e. bb. 51, 53, etc.). But beware of exaggerating the effect.

69.—*Tempo primo subito* at the *f*.

119*f*.—The Trio moves in long lines, in contrast to the shorter phrases of the Scherzo. The first strain consists of 8+10 bars; then 4+4+4+2+2+6+4+2, the final 2 also serving as the first 2 bars of the return.

133 & 177.—Though the pause on the barline is not in the autograph, it is so unexpected that it must have been an afterthought of Schubert's. It requires a very slight lengthening of the previous note (probably with pedal), followed by a momentary break in the sound. Apart from that, there should be no *rit*.

187–190.—A slight *rit*. to the double-bar; then *a tempo* at the *ff*.

IV   RONDO: ALLEGRO MODERATO [♩ = c. 120 & 100]

1*f* (♩ = c. 120).—In contrast to the light-hearted r.h. melody, the l.h. accompaniment should be impersonal, with light but precise staccatos, and accents no stronger than are needed to swing the rhythm along in half bars, as regular as clockwork. (The l.h. markings of b. 1 are of course meant to be continued.)

23.—The *pp* [*subito*] on beat 3 reflects a change of mood which lasts no longer than the middle of b. 25.

28.—Do no obscure the r.h. rest with pedal.

77.—The *fz* shows where the main theme returns. It requires a fresh attack—i.e. lift the hand very slightly before the A but without disrupting the rhythm.

2nd half of b. 104 (♩ = c. 100).—The beginning and end of this long central section (i.e. bb. 104–118 & 143–165) are relaxed in feeling as well as in tempo. The four upbeat quavers (8th-notes) in bb. 104, 106, 108, 112, etc., can even be slightly hesitant—but not those in bb. 109–111, which are part of a 4-bar phrase.

2nd half of b. 118.—The unexpectedly aggressive mood demands a slightly quicker and absolutely strict tempo—say, ♩ = c. 108;

142–143.—but here the tempo gradually relaxes, to return to ♩ = 100 at b. 144.

166–171.—A very gradual *accel*. towards [*Tempo primo* ♩ = c. 120, but *not* quicker] half way through b. 171. The editorial *fz* shows where the main theme returns. It again requires a fresh attack, as in b. 77.

199–201.—The music-box begins to run down during these three bars, which lead to

202 (♩ = c. 100).

210–211.—The two l.h. As move to the upper l.h. D.

12

8. SONATA in D
D. 850

SCHUBERT, Op. 53
August 1825

1) **Allegro**

In the footnotes to this Sonata: A = Schubert's autograph; B = the 1st edition, which appears to have been engraved from a manuscript that no longer exists.

1) B.1: in B the tempo mark is 'Allegro vivace' and the time-signature is C.

© 1979 by The Associated Board of the Royal Schools of Music

A.B. 1618b

(a) ♪

2) Bb. 34 & 37, l.h. notes 3-4: the slur is in B only.
3) Bb. 41 & 43, beats 3-4: thus in B;   A has even quavers.

A.B.1618b

un poco più lento e con cappriccio 4)

4) B. 48: B omits 'e con cappriccio'.
5) B. 56, r.h. note 8: B has E.
6) B. 58, r.h. notes 5 & 11: B has E,C.

16

A.B.1618b

8) B.167, beat 3: A has *sempre pp* stroked out; B has *p*.

9) B. 207, r.h. note 8: B has A.
10) B. 208, l.h. chord 1: in B the middle note is A.
11) B. 209, r.h. note 5: B has A.

12) B.242, r.h. notes 2 & 8: B has E; in A, where only beats 1 & 2 are written in full, note 2 could be either F or E; but b.91 shows that it was intended as F.

13) B.246: A has 'più Allⁿ' in pencil; B has 'un poco più mosso'.

14) B.251, r.h. chord 2, lowest note: B has B, not D.

15) B.257, r.h. chord 2: B omits the A.

Andante con moto [1]

(a)   (b) ♪   (c)   see preliminary Notes

1) B.1: in B the tempo mark is 'Con moto'.
2) B.31 chord 2 to b.32 chord 2: both hands an octave lower in A.
3) B.35, r.h. note 2: A adds F below the A.

4) B.46, r.h. chords 4-5: B omits the lower C, D.

5) B.51: 'mit Verschiebung' in B only.

6) B.52, r.h. upper note 5: B has C (without natural).

7) B.55, l.h. final chord: in B a semiquaver earlier.

8) B.57: B repeats this bar, probably mistakenly.

9) B.80, r.h. chord 6: B has natural to G, flat to G in b.82.

10) B.87, l.h. upper note 5: B has E.
11) B.98, r.h. chord 4: B omits the lower C (sharp).

12) B.105, l.h. chords 1-2: the main stave gives the A & B text. As the progression is very unSchubertian this may have been a slip. The Breitkopf *Gesammtausgabe* gives the emendation shown in small type, which the player may prefer.

13) B.114, r.h. note 2: B has a D below the G-natural.

14) B.127, l.h. chord 2: B has a semiquaver rest followed by a semiquaver.

A.B. 1618b

15) Bb.131-132, r.h. lower parts, final three chords: in B the rhythm is the same as in the l.h.
16) B.142, l.h. chords 1 & 2: B omits F.

[tre corde]

A.B.1618b

17) B.176, l.h. chords 2-5: B omits E.
18) Bb.181, 184: A omits 'un poco accel.' and 'a tempo'.
19) B.191, l.h. note 3: B omits *tr*.
20) B.193, l.h. notes 2-3: B has dotted-semiquaver, demi-semiquaver.

SCHERZO
Allegro vivace

1) B.8, 1.h. chord 1: both A & B have $\overset{\text{A}}{\underset{\text{A}}{\text{E}}}$ an octave below the r.h. Originally the previous chord in A was the same; then Schubert changed it, but forgot to alter b.8 to match.

2) B.22, chord 3: B omits the r.h. lower F, and has octave Bs in the 1.h.

3) B.51: 'Ped.' in B only.
4) Bb.64, 66 & 68, r.h. final chord: B adds an A between C & F.   In A the extra note is given in bb.66 & 68, which (with b.67) were
   a later interpolation.   It is missing in b.64.   The latter version is here preferred because it is more pianistic.   See also bb.318, 320
   & 322.
5) B.76, chord 3: B has r.h. upper note D, and l.h. B.

6) B.94, r.h. chords 2, 4 & 6: B misprints the middle part as C.
7) B.114: A has 'al segno Coda'.

TRIO

8) B.120, l.h. lowest line: thus in both A & B. The Breitkopf *Gesammtausgabe* substituted three Gs.

9) Bb.133 & 177: the pause is in B only.

10) B.178, r.h. chords 2-3: B adds D.
11) Bb.179 & 180, l.h. crotchets: B omits upper G.
12) B 190: A has 'D.C.'; in B the recapitulation is printed in full.

13) B. 266, beat 2: see footnote to b.76.

Coda

Pedale 15)   *Ped.*

14) Bb. 318, 320 & 322, r.h. final chord: B adds a C between E & A.
15) Bb. 323 & 327: A has only the first *Pedale*; B has *Ped.* in both bars.

A.B.1618 b

RONDO
Allegro moderato

(a) or as in the 1st edition. (b)

1) B. 3, r.h. beat 3: B omits ~.

A.B.1618b

2) B.30, r.h. chord 1: B omits D.

(c) 🎼 , or omit the ornament as in the 1st edition.

3) Bb. 78 & 95, r.h. note 3: B omits ⁓.

4) B. 80, r.h. notes 2-3: B ties the A's.

un poco più lento

45

(d) for small hands:

5) B.101, r.h. note 10: B has F.
6) B.103, r.h. note 10: B has F.
7) Bb.109 & 148, l.h. note 15: thus in A; B has B.

8) Bb.110 & 149, l.h. note 3: thus in A; B has A.
9) B.118, l.h. note 4: B has D.

10) B.156, l.h. note 3: thus in B; A has E (doubtless a slip).

48

11) B.165, l.h. notes 9 - 12: B has AEAE, as in b.164.
12) B.172, l.h. lower note 7: B has C (sharp).
13) B.174, l.h. chords 6 & 8: B adds D.

A.B.1618b

14) B.177, l.h. chords 6 & 8: B adds D.
15) B.180, r.h. note 1: B omits minim A.
16) B.191, l.h. chord 8: B adds D.

17) B.201: this bar is repeated in the Breitkopf & Härtel *Gesammtausgabe*; but not in either A or B.
18) B.202: A omits 'un poco più lento'.

SOURCES

A Autograph, including a title-page inscribed 'IV. Sonate' and dated October 1826. (London, British Library, Add. MS 36738.) Folios 6v & 10 (respectively the verso of the last page of the 1st movement and the recto of the first page of the 3rd) show the first and last pages of an early version of the Andante, here printed on pp. 84-85. Schubert crossed them out, removed the middle of the movement, and replaced it by three leaves (6 pages) containing the present version. Thus it can be seen that Schubert had completed the whole of the original Andante (and at least some of the rest of the work) before he realised that its second subject was not strong enough to provide sufficient contrast to the lyrical first subject.

B 1st edition: *Fantasie, Andante, Menuetto und Allegretto*, Op. 78; T. Haslinger, Vienna [1827], issued as Vol. 9 of the series *Musée Musical des Clavicinistes. Museum für Klaviermusik*. Dedicated by Schubert to his friend Joseph von Spaun. Haslinger provided the new title, presumably as a sales gimmick. The edition was engraved from A, as can be seen from the engraver's marks on the latter. It is a faithful copy, apart from increasing the number of accidentals, etc., omitted by Schubert. It does contain some extra slurs, however, and the words *Molto ligato* have been added to the Trio of the Menuetto; so Schubert must at least have glanced at the proofs.

The present edition follows A.

I MOLTO MODERATO E CANTABILE [♩ = c. 63 & 69]

For an explanation of the many editorial ties that have been added to the text, see the account of Schubert's idiosyncratic use of ties and slurs in the Introduction (p. 7) and in the Notes to the Sonata in D, D.850 (present volume, No. 8).

Bar 1, etc. (♩ = c. 63).—From the autograph it can be seen that Schubert at first wrote bb. 1-3 in common-time, thus :-

He then altered them to the present version and changed the time signature to $\frac{12}{8}$. His revised rhythm must be carefully preserved throughout the movement, with the short notes played as true semiquavers (16th-notes), i.e. one sixth the value of a dotted crotchet (quarter-note). Practise the figure slowly (counting six to every half bar), lighten each untied semiquaver chord, think of it as belonging to the following beat, and make sure that the latter is not delayed. When an accurate semiquaver has been achieved at this slow speed, the tempo can be increased step by step.

7, r.h. chords 4-5.—The problem for a small hand lies not so much in stretching chord 5 as in striking it accurately after the leap from chord 4. A possible alternative is shown in footnote (*a*).

13.—A change of colour is implied by the change to the major.

27-48) ♩.= c. 69).—Here, and wherever the same themes occur, the more lively mood requires a slight but imperceptible increase in speed.

47.—The l.h. continues the r.h. scale and *cresc*. A new voice enters (quietly) with r.h. beat 3, then makes a rapid *cresc.* to join the dynamic level of the l.h. by the end of the bar.

48.—Strictly in time, to allow the sound to thin out for the *p* in

49-52 & 57-64 (♩. = c. 63).—A return to the opening mood and tempo, which is momentarily interrupted by

52 beat 3-56 (♩. = c. 59).—Again strict tempo; but allow time at the end of b. 56 (fractionally prolonging the final chord with pedal), before 'placing' the *p* in b. 57.

65*f* (♩. = c. 69).—This aggressive version of the opening theme—and, indeed, the whole development as far as b. 113—requires the quicker of the two main tempi.

77-78.—Show the imitation between the two r.h. voices, the second of which enters in b. 77 with the high G F-natural, moves to the lower F on beat 4, then proceeds upwards in

quavers on beats 1 & 2 of b. 78, crossing voice 1 on the 2nd beat.

79-80.—The imitation is now between the r.h. upper part and the l.h. lower.

114-115 (♩. = c. 63).—A slight *rit.* is needed towards beat 3 of b. 115, followed by a compensating *accel.* to the recapitulation at b. 116.

II ANDANTE [♪ = c. 58, 76 & 69]

Imperceptible changes of tempo are again required to match the sharply contrasted themes. The tranquil main subject (bb. 1-30, etc.) could be ♪ = c. 58; the rough element of the 2nd group (bb. 31-39, 50-58, etc.) somewhat faster, ♪ = c. 76; and the gentle element (bb. 40-49, 59-76, etc.) half way between the two, ♪ = c. 69. As before, the different tempi should sound like changes in mood rather than noticeably contrasted speeds.

3, etc.—The r.h. turn is always part of the melodic line. It should be smooth and no louder than the surrounding notes.

47-49, r.h.—Whichever part happens to be moving is momentarily the more important of the two. In b. 48 the upper line is the same as in the previous bar, for the high F (sharp) of chord 3 is a Schubertian gleam of colour, not part of the melody. The tender feeling of the whole 3-bar phrase suggests that the gracenote in b. 49 should be long, as shown in footnote (*c*), rather than short.

58-61, r.h.—The 2-note 'upbeats' (like 'pre-echoes') are on a lower dynamic level than the main melody, which lies in the 3-note groups.

77-79.—The editorial *rit.* is suggested by Schubert's unattached *a tempo* two bars later.

119-121, r.h.—The main melody again lies in the 3-note groups, the paired semiquavers now being true echoes. But in b. 121 the 'echo' grows in intensity to become the melody itself.

III MENUETTO & TRIO: ALLEGRO MODERATO
[♩. = c. 60 & 54]

1, etc. (♩. = c. 60).—Lighten each group of four quavers, and think of it as an 'upbeat' leading to beat 1 of the following bar.

8-9 & 42-43.—After the heavy chord allow a fraction of time—but no break in the sound—before 'placing' the *p*.

53*f* (♩. = c. 54).—The lyrical Trio requires a more relaxed tempo, and suggests that a long appoggiatura was probably intended in bb. 58 & 75, as shown in footnote (*g*).

71-72.—A slight *rit.* would not be out of place, before picking up the tempo with the last three quavers of b. 72.

IV ALLEGRETTO [♩ = c. 92]

Resist the temptation to hurry this movement. It is one of those leisurely Schubert rondos that require all the time in the world (and a steady tempo) if their uncomplicated beauties are to be fully savoured.

1-2, etc.—The pair of r.h. upbeat quavers here and elsewhere must be phrased very clearly, . In Schubert's autograph the l.h. chords are differently tied and slurred at almost every appearance. He seems to have intended the bass fifths to be tied each time, with the probable exception of bb. 367-368, where the *ff* change of key will be underlined if they are restruck. In b. 2, etc., the minim C can be taken by the r.h. thumb, which also strikes the semibreve D of the treble stave.

3, etc.—Keep the fingers slightly tense and close to the keys for the repeated quaver chords. The rhythm should be extremely precise.

53-55.—A slight hesitation is needed here, before leading back to the tempo with the four upbeat quavers of b. 55.

52

123, notes 7–8.—Do not omit the accent and slur that heralds the l.h. return of the main theme.

178–180.—Again, a slight hesitation as in bb. 53–55.

191, etc.—The r.h. gracenotes come *before* the beat, otherwise the effect of an accent is lost.

211*f*.—Throughout the l.h. accompaniment of this melody the 1st quaver in each bar should be lightly detached—but never to the extent of sounding either hard or dry.

218 & 226.—It is better to take a fraction of time over the 2nd half of the bar than to make the r.h. flourish sound mechanical.

320.—The main theme again returns with the final pair of slurred quavers.

407.—A slight *rit.* is needed to slow down the tempo to

408.—*un poco più lento* ($\downharpoonright$ = c. 72), for a final backward glance at the theme, beginning with the last pair of quavers in b. 407.

[A facsimile of the autograph of this Sonata is to be published as Volume II of the forthcoming *British Library Music Facsimiles*.]

9. SONATA in G
D. 894

SCHUBERT, Op. 78
October 1826

Molto moderato e cantabile

(a) for small hands:

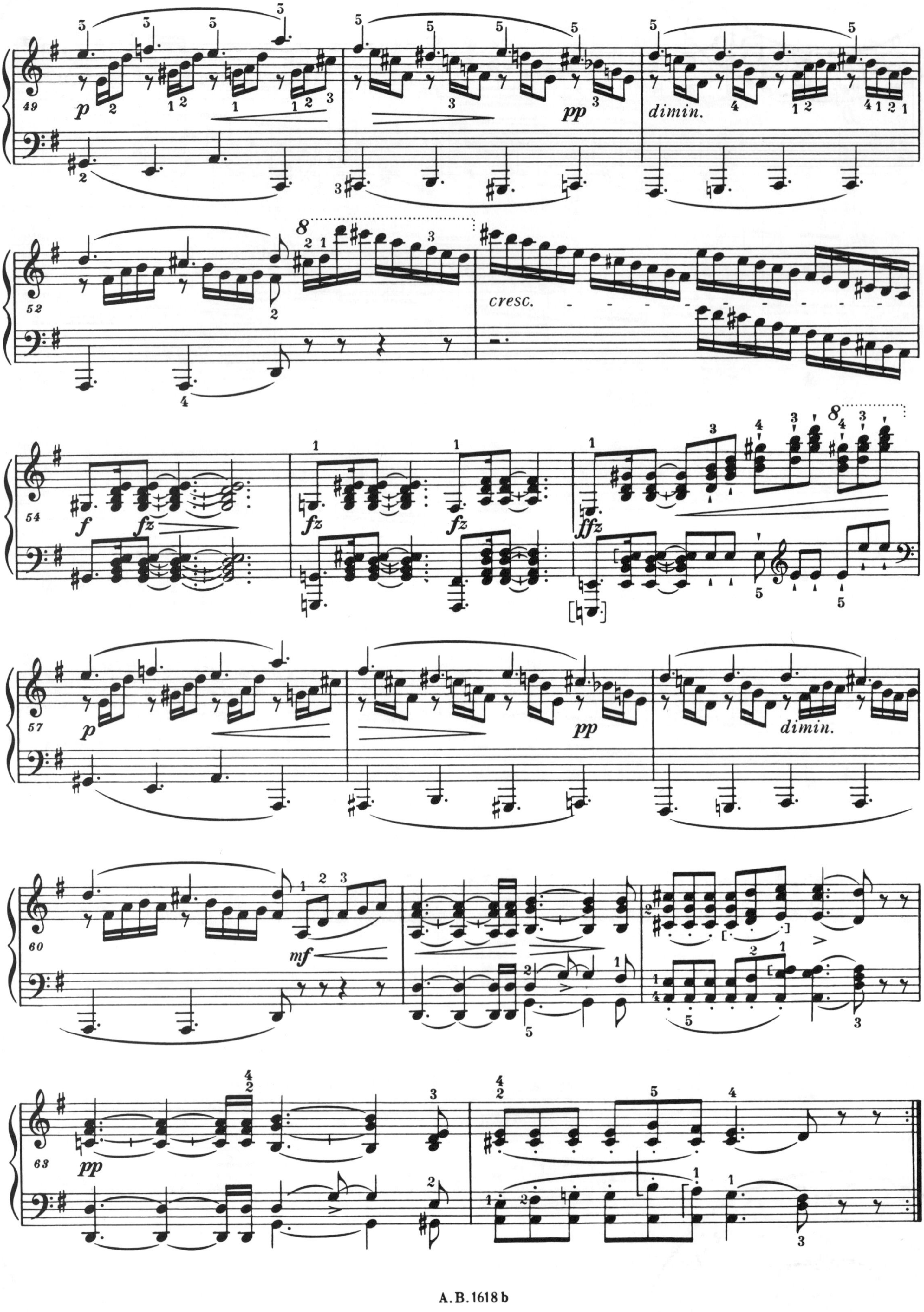
49
p
pp
dimin.
52
cresc.
54
f
fz
ffz
57
p
pp
dimin.
60
mf
63
pp

62

Andante

(f) for small hands:

MENUETTO
Allegro moderato

(a) for small hands: (b)   (c) small hands: omit the upper D of r.h. chord 3.   (d) small hands:

(e) small hands:

1) B. 55-56: *molto ligato* in 1st edition only.
2) B. 71: staccato dots in 1st edition only.

A.B.1618b

Allegretto

(c) gracenotes before the beat.

80

A.B.1618b

un poco più lento

SONATA in G
D. 894

Cancelled beginning and end of the original version of the 2nd movement

CANCELLED FIRST PAGE

The remaining leaves, except the last, were torn out of the autograph by Schubert, and replaced by the whole of the revised version of the movement.

CANCELLED LAST PAGE

10. SONATA in C Minor, D.958

A Autograph, headed 'Sonate I' and dated September 1828. (Basel, Collection of Dr Georg Floersheim. Microfilm: Washington, Library of Congress.)

B Autograph sketches. (Vienna, Stadtbibliothek, MH 170/c.) Eight pages containing:- I, bb. 1–98 (but 2 bb. shorter than A); II, complete (14 bb. shorter than A); III, complete (11 bb. shorter than A); IV, (a) bb. 1–91 (22 bb. shorter than A), and (b) bb. 245–388 (complete). All except IV (b) printed in *Gesammtausgabe, Revisionsbericht,* Series X, pp. 8–22; Breitkopf & Härtel, Leipzig 1897.

C 1st edition: No. 1 of *Franz Schubert's allerletzte Compositionen. Drei grosse Sonaten*; A. Diabelli, Vienna [1838]. Engraved from A, as shown by the engraver's marks on the latter. It follows the source closely, but adds many accidentals omitted by Schubert. He had intended to dedicate the three sonatas to J. N. Hummel; but when they eventually appeared, ten years after Schubert's death and one year after Hummel's, Diabelli dedicated them to Schumann.

The present edition follows A.

I Allegro [♩ = c. 116 & 104]

Bars 1–18 (♩ = c. 116).—The tempo of the defiant opening should be unwavering; but the rhetorical downward flourish in bb. 12–13 can be allowed some space. After the slightly hesitant bb. 14–16, the tempo picks up during the broken-octaves of bb. 17–18, and is firmly re-established by beat 1 of b. 19.

21–26.—The underlying sense of urgency will be enhanced if the l.h. semiquavers (16th-notes) are clearly articulated, and the 2-bar phrases are underlined by a slight *cresc.* towards, and *dim.* away from, beat 1 of every alternate bar.

27f.—With the *pp* there is a sudden relaxation of tension. Phrases grow longer (4–9 bars), and the l.h. dissolves into a background murmur pedalled in crotchets (quarter-notes). But the opening mood returns momentarily with the entry of the r.h. semiquavers in b. 36.

39f (♩ = c. 104).—An imperceptibly slower tempo is needed for the lyrical 2nd group—and, indeed, for most of the rest of the movement, apart from the return of the 1st group (b. 160f). The correct melodic line for bb. 44–53 is shown by the r.h. part in bb. 58–67. (On beat 2 of b. 52 note the change from the inner line to the upper.)

67f.—Do not over-stress the melody hidden in the lower r.h. semiquavers. It needs little or no pedal.

83.—A slight *rit.,* then *a tempo* on beat 1 of b. 84.

98.—*Subito f* with the l.h. F-sharp.

99f (♩ = c. 104).—Most of the development is based on new material. Admittedly there is a tenuous connection between the l.h. accompaniment in b. 103f and the r.h. figuration in b. 68, etc.; a clearer resemblance between bb. 115–116 and bb. 77–78; and an obvious reference to the opening rhythm in the l.h. of bb. 152–159. But the sinister, Verdi-like chromatic theme in bb. 119–151 is entirely new, and makes explicit the feeling of unease that lies behind so much of the 1st group.

271–272.—The bass line, G, E (flat), C, is important. Be specially careful of the E (flat), as the G immediately above it tends to be too loud.

II Adagio [♪ = c. 66, 72 & 80]

Three slightly different tempi are needed; but as usual they should be felt as changes of mood rather than of speed.

1f (♪ = c. 66).—The four beats in a bar should be slow enough to allow the hemi-demi-semiquavers (64th-notes) in b. 2 to sound unhurried, yet not so slow as to obscure the 4-bar phrasing.

18f (♪ = c. 72).—Slightly more movement, with a pedal change at each change of harmony.

28f (♪ = c. 80).—A further slight increase of movement. In the 1st edition each r.h. demi-semiquaver (32nd-note) is aligned with the 3rd note of a l.h. semiquaver-triplet; but there are three reasons for not following this convention in the present movement. Firstly, the autograph does not do so; secondly, the true rhythm has already been established in bb. 20 & 23; and thirdly, the rhythmic 'bite' of the theme would disappear if the demi-semiquaver were lengthened into a triplet-semiquaver.

43f (♪ = c. 66).

51–54.—Stress the *lower* line of the octave melody, to which b. 50 has been leading, and make sure that the tone remains consistent during the changes from hand to hand.

72–73.—The end of b. 72 needs to be drawn out slightly and followed by a fractional silence, before 'placing' the *p* of b. 73.

82f (♪ = c. 80).

94f (♪ = c. 66).—The melody lies in the middle of the r.h. as far as beat 1 of b. 101.

III Menuetto & Trio: Allegro [♩. = c. 66 & 60]

1–12 (♩. = c. 66).—The phrase-rhythm is oddly ambiguous. Though it undoubtedly consists of 3 times 4 bars, it is far from clear whether or not b. 1 is an 'up beat' bar. The return from the Trio suggests that it is not.

9.—*Subito p,* without any gap.

14f.—3+3+3+4+2 bars; then as in the 1st half, but with a silent bar added to each of the first two phrases.

46f (♩. = c. 60).—4-bar phrases throughout the Trio, except for the 6-bar group in bb. 63–68.

50.—The change of colour can be underlined by allowing the new voice (the r.h. upper line) to predominate slightly.

77.—Here the new voice enters with the lower r.h. line. When stressing it, make sure that the l.h. upper F on beat 3 of b. 78 is included in the melody.

IV Allegro [♩. = c. 132]

The structure of this vast rondo may be summarized thus:-

A	—	bridge	—	B	—	C	–
bb. 1–92		93–112		113–242		243–428	
C mi & ma		D♭		C♯ mi, etc.		B ma, etc.	
A	—	bridge	—	B + bridge	—	A + coda	
429-478		479–498		499–660		661–717	
(shortened)		(as before)		(as before, but)		(shortened)	
C mi & ma		D♭		B♭ mi, etc.		C mi	

The clue to the whole lies in the haunted unease, sudden crescendos, and stabbing accents of the opening subject. If these are given full value, and due note is taken of every deviation from the prevailing 4-bar phrase-structure, there will be no danger of the movement degenerating into a mindless tarantella.

1f.—No musical significance is to be attached to the difference in the r.h. notation used here and in b. 429f. From a pianistic point of view, however, the latter is the more helpful, for it shows that notes 2 & 4 in each bar should be thought of as belonging to the *following* note rather than the previous one. A touch of pedal can underline each *fz* and *fp*; otherwise none is needed.

92.—*Molto cresc.*

113f, l.h.—Lighten the quavers (8th-notes) and think of them as upward rather than downward movements of the hand.

145f, r.h.—Ditto.

153–156 & 165–168.—Pairs of 2-bar phrases to contrast with the 4-bar grouping.

197–212.—6+6+2+2 bars.

213–240.—Schubert's slurs are less consistent here than in the parallel passage, bb. 599–626. The phrase-structure beginning at b. 213 (*not* b. 214) is as follows:- 4+4+2+4, 4+4+2+4: thus each pair of r.h. dotted-crotchets forms an upbeat bar.

243–257 & 275–285.—Here, for the only times in the movement, the l.h. becomes a background murmur below the r.h. *cantabile*. Pedal in bars and half-bars with the changes of harmony.

258–274 & 286–301.—As a contrast to the preceding, a featherweight touch in both hands, and no pedal.

333–338 & 347–352.—Two 6-bar phrases.

353–413.—A long section of 3-bar phrasing, brought to an end by the 4-bar downward scale in b. 413*f*.

701*f*.—Do not rush the coda. It continues remorselessly until the very last bar.

1O. SONATA in C minor
D. 958

SCHUBERT
September 1828

Allegro

1) B.151; l.h. note 6: the lower D did not exist on Schubert's piano. If it is played here, in order to preserve the shape of the theme, the
upper D should be omitted.

Adagio

sempre ligato

(a)

(b) gracenotes before the beat, to preserve the accent on the octave Ds.

(c) it seems likely that in this movement the r.h. demisemiquavers should *not* coincide with the 3rd note of the l.h. triplets. See the preliminary Notes.

A.B.1618b

, i.e. start the arpeggios *on* the beat. Likewise in bb. 96 & 100-101, if
the large stretches have to be broken.

A.B.1618b

MENUETTO
Allegro

TRIO

Allegro

108

A. B. 1618 b

114

A.B.1618b

116

A. B. 1618b

1) Bb. 609-610: in the autograph the hairpin *cresc. & dim.* begin a bar later; but see bb. 603,617,623, etc.
2) B. 611, l.h. chord 4: the autograph has $\frac{E}{C}$ crotchet and a quaver rest —— a slip doubtless due to a turn of the page in the manuscript.

A Autograph, headed 'Sonate II'. [September 1828.] (Basel. Collection of Dr Georg Floersheim. Microfilm: Washington Library of Congress.)

B Autograph sketches. (Vienna, Stadtbibliothek, MH 171/c.) Sixteen pages in all. *Version* 1:- twelve pages containing I, bb. 1–132 (but 18 bb. shorter than A, with the bridge-passage to the 2nd group beginning in the tonic instead of the dominant. Page 2 includes a 2-line sketch of the coda of the 1st movement of D. 960); II, complete (61 bb. shorter than A); III, complete (1 b. shorter than A); IV, (a) bb. 1–36, plus 76 abortive bb., (b) bb. 48–243, (c) bb. 328–384 (2 bb. shorter than A). *Version* 2:- four pages of fair-copy of I, (a) bb. 1–65 (the bridge-passage still beginning in the tonic), (b) bb. 133–202 (1 b. longer than A), (c) bb. 335–361 (3 bb. shorter than A). The following are printed in the *Gesammtausgabe, Revisionsbericht,* Series X, pp. 22–34; Breitkopf & Härtel, Leipzig 1897:- *Version* 1:- I; middle 42 bb. of II; and the abortive 76 bb. of IV.

C 1st edition: No. 2 of *Franz Schubert's allerletzte Compositionen. Drei grosse Sonaten;* A. Diabelli, Vienna [1838]. Engraved from A, as shown by the engraver's marks on the latter. It follows the source closely, but adds many accidentals omitted by Schubert. He had intended to dedicate the three sonatas to J. N. Hummel; but when they eventually appeared, ten years after Schubert's death and one year after Hummel's, Diabelli dedicated them to Schumann.

The present edition follows A.

I Allegro [♩ = c. 126 & 138]

Two slightly different tempi are required; because the bridge-passage (bb. 28–53) between the 1st & 2nd groups, and the central section of the 2nd group itself (bb. 82–111), will lack urgency unless they are allowed to move on slightly.

Bars 1–6 (♩ = c. 126).—The r.h. octave As are less important than the inner parts that move in thirds. (The l.h. crotchets (quarter-notes) can each have a touch of pedal, but the rests must not be obscured.) In b. 6, however, it is the r.h. octaves that round-off the opening phrase with a slight *rit.,* followed by *a tempo* on b. 7.

7 & 9.—If preferred, the triplets can be divided alternately between the hands, though this is of course impossible in b. 11.

28*f* (♩ = c. 138).

34–39.—Underline this pair of 2½-bar phrases by moving the first towards beat 3 of b. 36, and making a slight dynamic drop on beat 4.

54.—*Poco rit.,* towards

55*f* (♩ = c. 126).—the opening tempo.

59 & 64.—Give full value to these 'extra' bars, and show the change to the minor in b. 62.

73.—A fraction of time can be allowed for rounding-off this echo bar before resuming the tempo in b. 74.

82, beat 1 (♩ = c. 138).—Only the low E is *f*; the upper three notes conclude the preceding *dimin.* Be specially careful of the l.h. G-sharp, which tends to be too loud.

105*f*.—Practise the r.h. slowly, a bar at a time, with the fingering shown. First play only notes 6–7; then notes 1–7; and finally notes 1–10. When they feel safe, the speed should be increased step by step.

116.—*Poco rit.,* as in b. 54.

117 (♩ = c. 126).

134–201.—The tempo remains unchanged for the development, during which the pulsating quaver (8th-note) chords are always subordinate to the remaining part(s). Be specially aware of the shift from C major to B major, and vice versa, in bb. 138–139, 143–144, etc.

188*f*.—When practising and playing wide leaps such as these, make sure that the hand arrives accurately above each note *before* it is struck. There is always more time than one imagines.

353*f*.—Divide the arpeggios between the hands in whatever way produces the quietest and smoothest wash of sound, keeping the pedal down from the beginning of b. 353 until almost the end of the pause in b. 354; likewise in bb. 355–356; then from the beginning of b. 357 until just before the chord in b. 360.

II Andantino [♪ = c. 84, 120 & 102]

Although no tempo changes are marked, the emotional range of the movement requires a correspondingly wide range of tempi. The central section (bb. 69–121) has no parallel among the piano sonatas. Its nearest equivalent in dramatic intensity is the central section in the slow movement of the String Quintet in C, D. 596, which dates from much the same period. There, however, a clearly defined theme and accompaniment fit into a single tempo; whereas here the improvisatory character of the music demands an altogether exceptional degree of rhythmic freedom.

1–68 (♪ = c. 84).—Nevertheless, an unwavering tempo best suits the gentle melancholy of the opening theme. The r.h. melody should stand out clearly above the l.h. accompaniment, which contains two distinct elements:- (a) the detached yet resonant bass notes initially marked with staccato dots—a touch of pedal on each will prevent them sounding dry; and (b) the slurred quavers (8th-notes), of which the first in each pair should be slightly stressed.

19*f* & 51*f*.—The shift to the relative major momentarily lightens the mood; but after only a few bars the prevailing melancholy returns and is intensified in bb. 27 & 59 by the sudden *fp* and the entry of an additional part in the upper line. (Bb. 13 & 45 show that the melody in bb. 27–30 & 59–62 is in the r.h. middle line.)

69–121 (♪ = c. 120).—A gradual *accel.* during bb. 69–72 leads to the new tempo. It is unstable, however, for it changes constantly during this central section in order to match the emotional and rhetorical implications of the impassioned music.

122–130.—At the climax of the storm there is a sudden collapse: backward-looking *ffz* chords alternate with snatches of a *p cantabile* that herald

131–158 (♪ = c. 102).—a less intense r.h. melody in and around the dominant. At first it is punctuated by rough *fz* chords (they should be unpedalled and spread fairly quickly); but from b. 147 the mood relaxes still further, and a new semiquaver (16th-note) figure appears in the accompaniment. A *rit.* during bb. 157–158 leads to

159*f* (♪ = c. 84).—the recapitulation. The semiquaver figure is continued in the l.h., as a link with the preceding section, while a triplet monotone above the r.h. melody adds a desolate fourth part to the original three. The increase in rhythmic movement does not last, however, for at b. 177 the l.h. accompaniment reverts to its original paired quavers, and the r.h. triplets become single bell-notes. Yet there is one more passionate outburst, in bb. 185–188, before the melody finally vanishes in the ghostly chords of bb. 196–200. No *rit.* is needed: for the movement should simply fade away on the last two bare octaves.

III Scherzo: Allegro vivace [♩. = c. 66] & [Trio]: Un poco più lento [♩. = c. 44]

1–6, etc. (♩. = c. 66).—Crisp accented arpeggios, to contrast with the light staccato on the remaining 3-part chords. When practising the r.h. leap from b. 2 to b. 3, etc., at first make a silent comma at the barline; then, when the passage is secure, the comma can be gradually shortened and finally eliminated. In b. 6 note that the l.h. chord is *not* a dotted crotchet.

33.—Round-off the *decresc.* with a very slight *rit.;* then strictly *a tempo* for the *ff* in b. 34.

72–79.—Do not mask any of the rests with pedal.

80*f* (♩. = c. 44).—Though the Trio is marked only *Un*

poco più lento, it needs to be considerably slower than the Scherzo. The r.h. is *legato cantabile* throughout. When pedal is used, it must not smudge the l.h. staccatos.

96, beat 1.—If the l.h. *fz* F-natural is played staccato it will not obscure the legato D of the r.h. melody.

103.—Be specially aware of the l.h. C-natural, for that is the note which signals the approaching end of the Trio.

IV Rondo: Allegretto [♩ = c. 120 & 132]

Schubert also used the opening theme—though with an entirely different effect—in the slow movement of the Sonata in A minor, D. 537 (Vol. 1, No. 2).

1*f* (♩ = c. 120).—Let the r.h. top line sing out effortlessly. As the r.h. rests must not be obscured with pedal, be careful to sustain the tone by holding the l.h. minims (half-notes) for their full value.

11.—Here half-bar pedalling is needed because of the wide l.h. stretches. Likewise in the 2nd half of b. 12 and the 1st half of b. 14.

13.—*Subito p,* because the previous [*poco*] *cresc.* continues to b. 12.

18*f*.—For the new layout of the melody, think of a warm unison of violas and clarinets in the l.h. top line. The r.h. triplets should flow smoothly and unobtrusively in the background.

30, etc.—In accordance with the old convention, the dotted rhythm here and elsewhere in the movement should be adjusted to coincide with the prevailing triplet rhythm, as shown above the stave. The two notes concerned are generally aligned thus in the autograph, and always in the 1st edition.

36–37.—Allow a fraction of time for the r.h. leap from one bar to the next, sustaining the sound with pedal.

47.—Pedal the 1st half of the bar, but not the 2nd half.

48*f*.—The quiet background triplets must never sound dry. Discreet pedal can be used at times; but when this is in-

admissible—for example, during the r.h. staccato quavers in bb. 49–50, etc.—the notes of the triplets can be played with *tenuto* touch: i.e. held down for longer than their true value (provided the harmony does not change).

63–69.—Pedal the 1st half of each bar, then a touch on beats 3 & 4.

94–101.—In the r.h., think of one group of instruments playing the repeated G-naturals, and another group answering more quietly until, in b. 102, the second group begins to take over the main role.

107.—Do not obscure the rest with pedal.

119–127.—Strict tempo, except for a slight hesitation in b. 127 to show that the main theme is at last about to return.

148–213 (♩ = c. 132).—Though the central section is so closely related to the opening theme, its very different character requires a slightly quicker tempo. Much of it is in 7-bar phrases, generally divided into 2+5 bars. B. 213 leads, with a *rit.,* into

214*f* (♩ = c. 120).—a magical 'false return' in F-sharp. During the *ritard.* in bb. 220-222 the harmony gradually shifts towards A major and

223*f*.—the true return.

328.—If sufficient *dim.* has been made there will be no need for a *rit.*

335–343.—The effect here should be of temporarily losing the way. Having slipped into the minor, the theme unexpectedly finds itself poised on the dominant of F (b. 337). After a pause for reflection it continues in and around F (bb. 339–342), but decides that that's not quite right. Another pause, and the way begins to grow clear (b. 344). Finally (b. 346) the right path is regained, only to end abruptly on the brink of

351*f* (♩ = c. 144).—the coda. Though marked Presto, it is not so very much quicker than the main tempo.

379*f*.—Do the concluding bars refer to the beginning of the whole sonata? It almost seems so because of the striking similarity of their octave leaps, pedal As, unexpected G-naturals, and inner parts moving stepwise in 3rds.

II. SONATA in A

D. 959

SCHUBERT
September 1828

1) B.16, beat 1: *p* in the autograph; but see the more probable b. 217.

A.B.1618b

2) B.208, l.h. note 1: thus in the autograph; not D, as in b.7.

3) B.254, r.h. note 1: the B is missing in the autograph, but see b.49.

Andantino

140

1) Bb. 93, 102 & 104, r.h.: the autograph has a *simile* sign (⁒) meaning 'repeat the previous bar'; the 1st edition interprets this, probably correctly, as shown above.

SCHERZO
Allegro vivace

(a) ♪   1) Bb. 7-8, r.h.: the autograph sketch has

2) B.71, r.h. chord 1: thus in the autograph; the 1st edition, followed by the *Gesammtausgabe,* and later editions, printed it an octave too high.

A.B.1618b

146

[TRIO]

Un poco più lento

RONDO
Allegretto

1) B. 255, l.h. chord 1: crotchet in the autograph; but see r.h. and b.43.

A.B.1618 b

160

A.B.1618 b

12. SONATA in B flat, D.960

A Autograph, headed 'Sonate III' and dated 26 September 1828 at the foot of the final page. (Basel, Collection of Dr Georg Floersheim. Microfilm: Washington, Library of Congress.)

B Autograph sketches. (Vienna, Stadtbibliothek, MH 172/c.) Ten pages containing: I, (a) bb. 1–206 (but 37 bb. shorter than A), (b) bb. 207–224 (6 bb. shorter than A) on p. 3 of IV, (c) bb. 342–366 (2 bb. shorter than A) on p. 2 of I of Sontata in A, D.959; II, complete (15 bb. shorter than A, and with a different middle section); III, complete (Scherzo 16 bb. shorter than A, and lacking Coda); IV, (a) bb. 148–229 (4 bb. shorter than A), (b) bb. 254–315 (10 bb. shorter than A), (c) bb. 489–540 (4 bb. shorter than A). The following are printed in the *Gesammtausgabe, Revisionsbericht,* Series X, pp. 34–43; Breitkopf & Härtel, Leipzig 1897:- I (a) first 113 bb, II the cancelled middle section.

C 1st edition: No. 3 of *Franz Schubert's allerletzte Compositionen. Drei grosse Sonaten;* A. Diabelli, Vienna [1838]. Engraved from A, as shown by the engraver's marks on the latter. It follows the source closely, but adds many accidentals omitted by Schubert. He had intended to dedicate the three sonatas to J. N. Hummel; but when they eventually appeared, ten years after Schubert's death and one year after Hummel's, Diabelli dedicated them to Schumann.

The present edition follows A.

I Molto moderato [♩ = c. 108 & 116]

A slight relaxation of the main tempo is needed at the following points of the exposition and recapitulation: (a) wherever the spacious main theme (interrupted by mysterious bass shakes) appears in the tonic; and (b) during the broken phrases of the closing section (bb. 99–116 & 327f).

Bars 1–18 (♩ = c. 108).—Though the r.h. octave melody is the most important element of the texture, do not forget the l.h. middle line that shadows it in 6ths. The distant thunder of the l.h. shake in b. 8 should never rise above *pp*. To control it, keep the keys half-depressed throughout. (The need for pedal depends on the instrument and the resonance of the room or hall in which it is being played.) The change of harmony beginning on beat 4 of b. 13 suggests a *cresc.* towards, and gradual *dim.* away from, beat 1 of b. 15.

19, l.h. beats 1–3.—Schubert's notation implies a demi-semiquaver (32nd-note) shake; but it is better to play fewer notes than to allow an increase in dynamics.

20f (♩ = c. 116).—Keep the l.h. light, and pedal with the changes of harmony.

35, beat 4 (♩ = c. 108).—A slight broadening of beats 1–3 is needed to lead into the *f* return of the theme.

48–58 (♩ = c. 116).—As can be seen from b. 59f, the melody is in the l.h. upper part. Keep the r.h. wrist loose, and allow the hand to rock slightly (from r. to l. and back again) during each crotchet (quarter-note). If the r.h. cannot stretch beat 3 of b. 51 while holding the top F-sharp, the As of the triplet can be omitted. Likewise the C-sharps of the triplets on beats 1 & 2 of b. 52.

65–66.—Each r.h. semiquaver (16th-note) belongs to the *following* dotted quaver (8th-note).

80f.—No pedal; and do not allow the triplets to hurry.

91–92.—A fractional gap between the two bars will not be noticed if a *dim.* is made during beats 3–4 of b. 91.

99–116 (♩ = c. 108).—The broken phrases require a slight slackening of the tempo. In bb. 103–105 the editorial arpeggios are copied from bb. 331–333; but note that (to increase the climax) the final l.h. chord is *not* broken. It should coincide with the lower C of the r.h. arpeggio.

117–125.—In performance the repeat of the exposition should be made whenever possible, for the 1st-time bars reveal fresh aspects of the opening theme. (Notes 2–3 of the latter contain the germ of the clipped semiquavers in b. 117, etc.; and the distant rumbling of b. 8 becomes the terrifying thunder-clap of b. 124.) Two tempi alternate, the slower for the

backward-looking bb. 118 & 120. During b. 124 a *rit.* is needed to allow time for the thunder-clap to fade away.

127f (♩ = c. 116).

168–181.—As the harmonic movement and excitement increase, the tempo moves on slightly;

182.—but having reached its temporary goal of D minor, it immediately reverts to ♩ = c. 116.

183–261.—In the long passage of suspense that follows, hints of the opening theme and the key of the dominant appear and disappear. (Do not alter the tone and balance of the repeated quaver chords as they pass from hand to hand in bb. 188, 196, etc.) But the outcome remains uncertain until

212f.—where the *fp* dominant-7th steers the harmony unmistakably in the direction of B-flat. Before arriving there, however, a dozen meditative bars intervene, with something of the effect of a measured cadenza. And finally the mysterious bass shake once again leads to a pause; which is followed by

224, beat 4 (♩ = c. 108).—the recapitulation.

II Andante sostenuto [♩ = c. 52 & 58]

1–42 (♩ = c. 52).—Aim at achieving a sound similar to that at the opening of the slow movement of the String Quintet in C, D. 956, where the three inner instruments sustain a ravishing, harmonized melody *pp*, while the 1st violin and cello add fragmentary comments above and below it. Schubert's *con pedale* should not be interpreted as a licence to obscure the rests. Its twofold purpose is to prevent the l.h. from sounding dry and to help the r.h. attain a seamless legato. Pedal should therefore be used with discretion, and never for longer than a quaver at a time. L.h. note 2 is always a demi-semiquaver (32nd-note); so it comes *after* the r.h. semiquaver in bb. 9–12, etc.

10 & 99, r.h. chord 1.—There is no accidental to the F in either the sketch or the finished autograph: yet the chord sounds un-Schubertian with an F-sharp, as demanded by the key-signature. In view of Schubert's inveterate habit of omitting obvious accidentals—see, for example, bb. 45–46 of the 1st movement, where the flat is missing from every A—it seems not unlikely that a double-sharp to the F was intended, but forgotten simply because it *was* so obvious. One cannot be certain, however; so each player must decide for himself whether he prefers an F-sharp or an F-double-sharp.

43–88 (♩ = c. 58).—The middle section needs a slight increase in tempo.

51f.—The r.h. upper line should sing out effortlessly. Keep a loose wrist, and play the sextuplets lightly and absolutely evenly.

52, etc.—In Schubert's autograph (and the 1st edition) the r.h. demi-semiquavers are all carefully aligned with the sixth note of the sextuplets, following the old convention that dotted rhythms in duple time should be adjusted to coincide with prevailing triplets.

90–122 (♩ = c. 52).—The new l.h. figure should be slightly more prominent than its three companion quavers.

123f.—This magical change to the tonic major can be underlined by a slight relaxation of the tempo. There should be no additional *rit.,* however, until the penultimate bar.

III Scherzo & Trio: Allegro vivace con delicatezza [♩. = c. 72]

1f.—The combination of vivacity and delicacy provides the key to this Scherzo. Keep the quaver accompaniment light in whichever hand it occurs, and concentrate on its middle line. (The two outer lines will take care of themselves.)

33f.—Very precise l.h. staccatos—think of note 2 in each bar as a stretch rather than a leap—with crisply accentuated arpeggios in the r.h. The r.h. 2-bar rests (which are not in the sketch) quaintly extend the normal 4-bar pattern: first of all to 3 times 6; then to twice 5; and finally back to 4—but with the addition of an unexpected 2-bar overlap (bb. 67–68) that decorates the previous two bars while anticipating the bar that follows.

98*f.*—In the sombre Trio the *fzp* accents in the l.h. should be fairly heavy, with a touch of pedal on each to make it 'broad' rather than rough. The one in b. 122 is louder than the rest. Do not begin too quietly or there will be no room for the *pp* [*subito*] in b. 103.

IV ALLEGRO MA NON TROPPO [♩ = c. 112, 120 & 132]

1*f* (♩ = c. 112).—The nagging *fp* octave G continually thwarts the effort to escape from the alien, overcast atmosphere of C minor to the more carefree and sunny regions of the tonic. Its relentless insistence can be stressed by slightly exaggerating the preceding quaver rest and fractionally delaying the following r.h. entry.

86*f.*—As in b. 51*f* of the slow movement, keep the r.h. wrist loose, lighten the semiquavers, and allow the hand to rock slightly as it follows the pattern of the figuration. There can be a touch of pedal on each crotchet, but not enough to prolong the l.h. quavers. Bb. 87–91, etc., will be found less difficult when played exactly as written: i.e. if the 1st semi-quaver in each group is held for no longer than its written value.

156*f* (♩ = c. 120).—The whole of this second half of the 2nd subject group can move on slightly.

185*f.*—Though the 1st edition aligns the r.h. semiquavers with the 3rd note of the l.h. triplets, the autograph rarely does so and apparently only accidentally. Since the true dotted rhythm has already been established in bb. 168–185, it seems likely that it should continue unchanged in bb. 185–221, and *not* be adjusted to coincide with the prevailing triplets.

224*f* (♩ = c. 112).—Note that in bb. 225–229 & 234–238 (but nowhere else in the movement) the r.h. upbeat in every second bar is a semiquaver, not a quaver. This establishes its connection with the rhythm of the previous section.

255*f* (♩ = c. 132).—The stormy development requires a marked increase of tempo; but it begins to relax again from about b. 306, until it returns to *tempo primo* (♩ = c. 112) at b. 312.

b. 293*f.*—If the 1st r.h. chord cannot be stretched in bb. 293 & 295, and (particularly) bb. 299, 301 & 303, omit the *top* note. (It will be supplied by the listener's imagination.)

512*f* (♩ = c. 160).—If the Presto is played too quickly its relationship to the opening theme will be lost. No *accel.* is needed, even during the final bars.

12. SONATA in B flat
D. 960

SCHUBERT
September 1828

Molto moderato

(a) a demi-semiquaver (32nd-note) shake; but see the preliminary Notes.

(b) 𝄐

Andante sostenuto

1) Bb. 41-42: the r.h. chords are tied in the sketch and the 1st edition, but (surprisingly) not in the autograph.

2) B.86, r.h. lower line, notes 12 & 14 : unmistakable Ds in the autograph. The 1st edition gives Cs. In the sketch the passage is quite different.

A.B.1618 b

A.B. 1618 b

3) B.109, r.h. chord 1: the 1st edition omits the C♮.

4) B.124 l.h. note 1: the autograph mistakenly has G.

A.B.1618 b

SCHERZO
Allegro vivace con delicatezza

(a) The Coda is not played until the end of the Da Capo of the Scherzo, when it replaces the 1st- and 2nd-time bars.

A.B.1618b

TRIO

Allegro ma non troppo

(a) It seems likely that in this movement the r.h. semiquavers should *not* coincide with the 3rd note of the l.h. triplets. See the preliminary Notes.

1) B.247, l.h. chord 2: thus in the autograph (i.e. differing from b.24).

Presto

Wien, den 26. Sept. 1828
[Vienna, the 26th Sept. 1828]

1:07 A.B.1618b